1. Light

What light can do

Light lets us see ourselves.

Light lets us see the world around us.

Light lets us see things beyond our world.

Light travels in straight lines.

Some things make their own light.

Q1 Look carefully at the picture. Make a list of the things in the picture that:
a make light
b help us to see things
c protect us from sunlight.

1. Light

Light on the move

▲ Light travels in straight lines. Light travels very fast. It travels 300 million metres every second.

▲ Light from the sun takes more than eight minutes to reach us on the Earth.

Light and sound

Light travels much faster than sound.

◄ In a storm, the thunder and the lightning happen at the same time. The light travels so quickly that we see it almost straightaway. The sound takes a lot longer to travel, so we hear the thunder after we see the lightning.

You can work out how far away a thunderstorm is from you. Count how many seconds there are between the lightning and the thunder. Divide your number by three, and that is the distance to the storm in kilometres.

Q1 At the beginning of a race you can sometimes see the runners setting off before you hear the starting gun. Explain why this happens.

Q2 You see some lightning, and six seconds later you hear the thunder. How far away is the thunderstorm?

2. Shadows and colours

Light and shadows

Some materials (like glass) let light go straight through them. They are **transparent**.

Some materials (like tracing paper) let a bit of light go through them. They are **translucent**.

Some materials do not let any light go through them. They are **opaque**. Opaque materials make shadows.

You can test materials by shining a torch at them. Use a ray box if you do not have a torch.

Q1 Copy this table.

Material	Opaque	Transparent	Translucent

Apparatus

- torch ■ box of materials
- clamp and stand

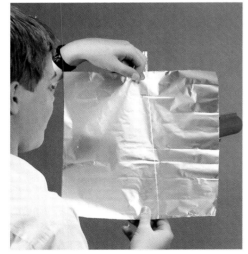

A Hold the material between the torch and your eyes. If you cannot see the torch, the material is opaque.

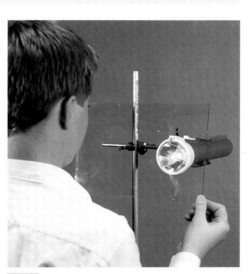

B If you can see the torch clearly the material is transparent.

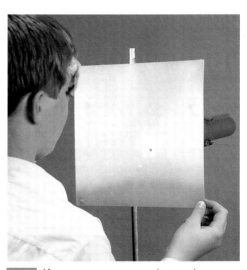

C If you can see only a glow from the torch the material is translucent.

D Repeat the test with the other materials. Record the results in your table.

Q2 Which material would you use for windows in a changing room? Explain why.

Extension exercise 1 can be used now.

Making rainbows

Ordinary light is white light. White light is made up of different colours. You can make a rainbow out of white light. You will use a **prism**.

Apparatus

■ 3 ray boxes ■ single slit
■ power pack ■ prism ■ white card
■ red, green and blue filters

A Shine the light from the ray box through the prism. Move the prism and the card until you can see a rainbow.

Red
Orange
Yellow
Green
Blue
Indigo
Violet

▲ The rainbow pattern you can see is called a **spectrum**. The colours in it are red, orange, yellow, green, blue, indigo, and violet. The first letters of the words in the following sentence are the same as the first letters of the colours: **R**ichard **O**f **Y**ork **G**ave **B**attle **I**n **V**ain.
This will help you to remember the order of the colours in a rainbow.

Making coloured light

A piece of coloured glass or plastic is called a **filter**.
You can make coloured light using a filter.
A filter lets only one colour of light go through it.

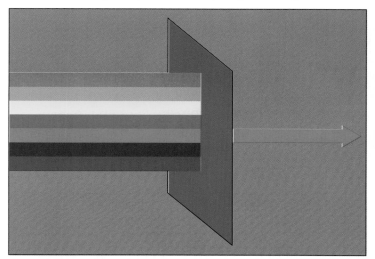

▲ The blue filter lets only blue light through.

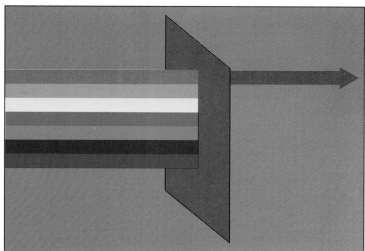

▲ The red filter lets only red light through.

Let us see what happens when you mix different coloured lights. Mixing lights is not the same as mixing paints.

Q1 Copy this table.

Colours	Appearance when mixed
Red + green	
Red + blue	
Green + blue	
Red + green + blue	

A Make red light by putting a red filter in front of your ray box.

B Use another ray box and make green light by putting a green filter in front of your ray box.

C Mix red and green light by pointing both of your ray boxes at the card. Complete the table.

D Repeat **A** to **C** for the other colours in the table. You will need three ray boxes for the last row in the table.

E If you have time, test some different colours.

Q2 Write down all the colours of the rainbow, in the right order.

Q3 How can you make white light from coloured light?

2. Shadows and colours

How we see things

► When light shines on an object, some of it bounces off (**reflects**). Some of this light goes into our eyes and we see the object.

Some materials show up better than others in dim light. This is because some materials reflect more light than others.

▲ These two children are going for a cycle ride.

▲This is what the children look like when it is getting dark.

Q1 Look at the two photographs of children.
  a Which person has the better clothes for cycling at night? Explain why.
  b Which bicycle is safer for cycling at night? Explain why.

Seeing colours

Most materials reflect only part of the light that shines on them.
They **absorb** the rest of the light.

Coloured objects reflect some of the colours that shine on them.
The other colours are absorbed.

▲ Blue objects reflect blue light. They absorb all the other colours.

▲ Yellow objects reflect yellow light. They absorb all the other colours.

▲ White objects reflect all the colours.

▲ Black objects do not reflect any of the colours. All the colours are absorbed.

Q1 Draw coloured pictures to show:
  a why red objects look red
  b why grass looks green.

2. Shadows and colours

Using coloured light

Let us see what happens when we look at coloured things in coloured light.

Q1 Copy this table.

Colour on strip	In red light it looks ...	In blue light it looks ...	In green light it looks ...

Apparatus

- ray box ■ power pack
- red, green and blue filters

A Make coloured light by putting a red filter in front of a ray box.

B Look at the colours on the edge of this page. Notice what colour they are in red light. Complete the table.

C Repeat **A** and **B** with a blue filter, and then with a green filter.

Q2 Why do coloured clothes look different in discos with coloured lights?

black

white

red

orange

yellow

green

blue

indigo

violet

3. Reflection and refraction

Mirrors

Some shiny things reflect so well that we can see things in them. The picture we see in a mirror is called an **image**.

Try these things with mirrors.

Apparatus

■ 2 flat mirrors

A Stand in front of a friend and hold a mirror so that you can see your face. Both of you close your right eye. Draw a picture to show your friend's face and your face in the mirror.

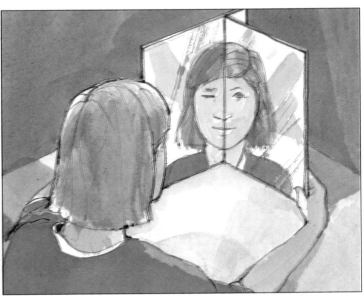

B Hold two mirrors together at 90 degrees. Look at your face in the mirror. Close your right eye. This is how other people see you.

Spot the dog and a little green frog
Looked at themselves in a mirror
Spot put his paw on the dog that he saw
And the frog just gave a shiver

Spot thought he was with a dog and two frogs
The frog was afraid when he saw two dogs
And hopped away with a quiver

C You can use mirrors to make a secret code. Try to read this code writing.

D Now write your own mirror message. See if your friend can read it.

3. Reflection and refraction

Seeing around corners

Mirrors can help you to see around corners.
You can see around corners using a **periscope**.

▲ The periscope uses two mirrors to bend the light.

You can make a periscope for yourself. Ask your teacher for the periscope copymaster.

Apparatus

- 2 plastic mirrors ■ scissors
- periscope copymaster
- Blu-Tack ■ sticky tape

A Carefully cut out the shape on the card. Fold the card along the dotted lines.

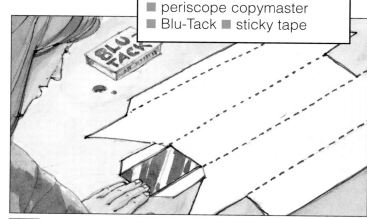

B Stick two mirrors onto the card using Blu-Tack.

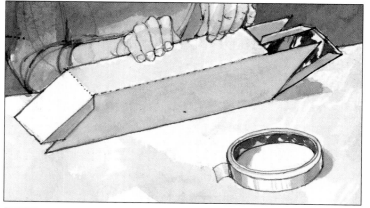

C Fold the card so that the mirrors are on the inside. Stick down flap **A** using sticky tape.

D Stick down flaps **B** and **C**. Try out your periscope.

Q1 Why do cars have mirrors for the driver to use?

Q2 Why do submarines use periscopes?

Investigating mirrors

Let us find out how light is reflected from mirrors.
We will measure the angles of the rays of light.

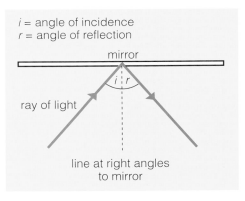

i = angle of incidence
r = angle of reflection

mirror

ray of light

line at right angles
to mirror

Q1 Copy this table.

Angle of incidence	Angle of reflection

Apparatus

- flat mirror and support
- ray box ■ single slit
- power pack ■ plain paper
- ruler ■ protractor

A Stand the mirror on a piece of paper. Draw a line along the back of the mirror.

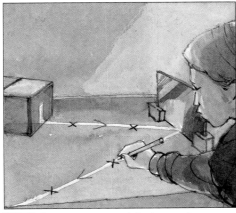

B Shine a ray of light at the mirror. Mark the rays of light with crosses and arrows. Put two crosses on each ray.

C Take away the mirror. Use a ruler to draw lines through the crosses.

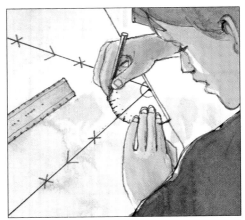

D Use a protractor to draw a line at 90° to the mirror.

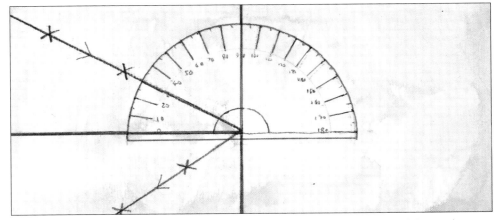

E Measure the angle the ray goes in at (**the angle of incidence**) and the angle it comes out at (**the angle of reflection**).
Record the angles in your table.

F Repeat **A** to **E** three more times. Shine the light at different angles.

Q2 What do you notice about the two sets of angles?

Extension exercises 2 and 3 can be used now.

Bending light

Light travels in straight lines. Sometimes we can make light bend. This is called **refraction**.

Apparatus

■ mug ■ coin ■ beaker
■ pencil

A Put a coin in the bottom of a mug. Move your head so that the coin is just out of sight.

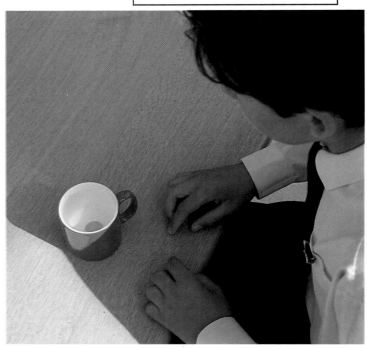

B Keep your head still. Ask a friend to fill the mug with water. Look to see if the coin reappears.

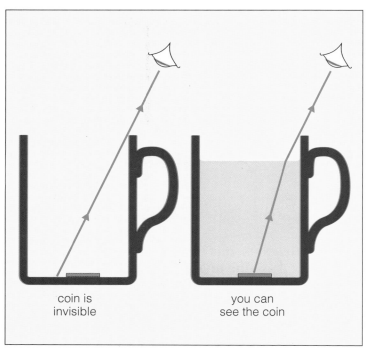

coin is invisible   you can see the coin

▲ You can see the coin because the light bends as it comes out of the water.

C Fill a beaker with water and stand a pencil in it. Look carefully at the pencil. It looks as if it bends where it goes into the water.

Glass and perspex can bend light too.
Let us investigate what happens when light goes through a glass block.

A Put a glass block on a piece of paper. Draw around the block.

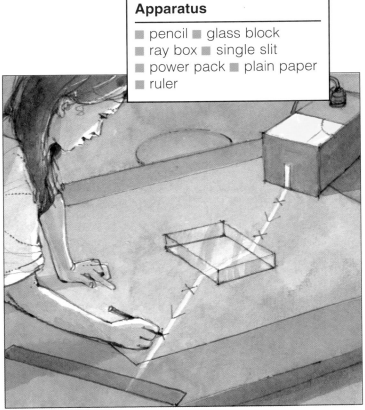

B Shine a ray of light at the block. Mark the rays of light with crosses.

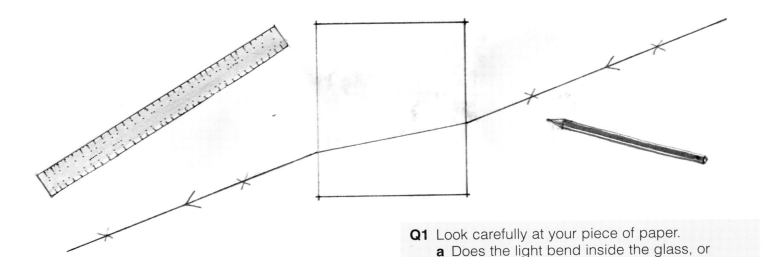

C Take the block away. Use a ruler to join the crosses.

Q1 Look carefully at your piece of paper.
a Does the light bend inside the glass, or where it goes into the glass?
b Where else does it bend?

Q2 What do you notice about the way the light bends when it goes into the glass, and when it comes out?

Total internal reflection

Let us see how light bends when it goes through a semi-circular piece of glass.

Apparatus
- semi-circular glass block
- ray box ■ single slit
- power pack ■ plain paper
- pencil ■ ruler

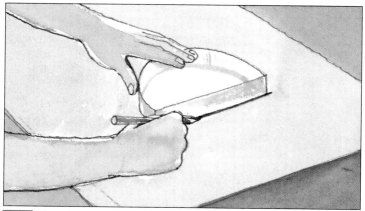

A Put the glass block on a piece of paper and draw round it. Mark the middle of the straight side.

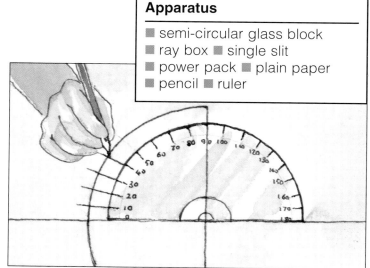

B Draw a line at right angles to the straight side. Mark five angles of 10° from this line.

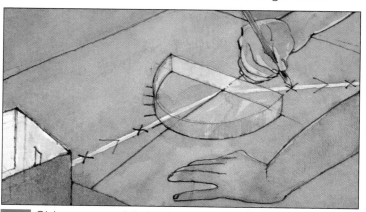

C Shine a ray of light through the glass block along your first 10° line. Aim it at the mark you made in the middle of the straight side. Mark the light beam with crosses.

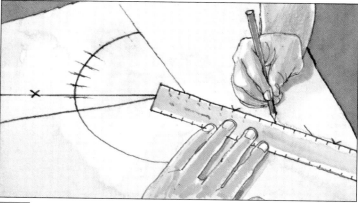

D Take the glass block away and use a ruler to mark where the ray of light went.

E Put the glass block back onto the paper. Repeat **C** and **D** for the other 10° lines.

▼ As you move the ray box around, the ray of light gets refracted more and more. Eventually it is bent so much that it cannot come out of the flat edge of the block. It is reflected inside the block (**internally**). This is called **total internal reflection**, because all the light is reflected inside the glass.

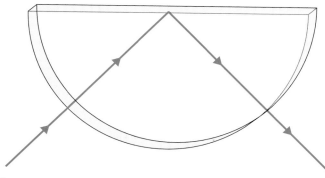

Q1 Describe what happened to the ray of light when you moved the ray box around the semi-circular block.

Extension exercise 4 can be used now.

Lenses

Lenses are curved pieces of glass or perspex. They are used to bend light.

There are two different kinds of lens.

Apparatus

- ray box set up for parallel light
- triple slit ■ power pack
- fat and thin convex lenses
- concave lens ■ plain paper ■ ruler

▲ **Diverging** (or **concave**) lenses make light spread out.

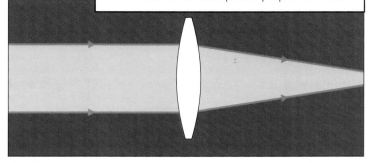

▲ **Converging** (or **convex**) lenses make the light bend inwards.

You can see what happens with different lenses.

A Stand a thin convex lens on a piece of paper. Draw around the lens.

B Shine three rays of light at the middle of the lens. Mark the rays of light with crosses. Take the lens away. Join up the crosses.

C Repeat **A** and **B** with a fat convex lens.

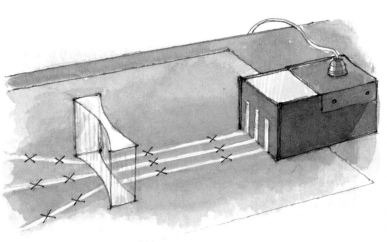

D Repeat **A** and **B** with a concave lens.

Q1 What happens to rays of light when they go through:
   a a thin convex lens?
   b a fat convex lens?
   c a concave lens?

Q2 Which bend light the most: fat lenses or thin lenses?

Q3 What would happen if you had used a thin concave lens in **A** and **B**?

4. Using light

Cameras

A **pinhole camera** is a very simple camera. Light goes into the camera through a pinhole. You can see the image by looking at the screen. Let us find out how it works.

Q1 Copy this table.

Number of holes	Large or small holes?	Bright or dim image?	Upside-down or upright?	Sharp or blurred?
1	small			
2	small			
1	large			

A Use a pin to make a small hole in the foil at the front of the camera.

B Work in a darkened room. Point the pinhole end of the camera at the lamp. Look at the screen. Complete the table.

C The image is very dim. Make another hole near the first one. Point the camera at the lamp again. Complete the table.

D Make a much bigger hole in the foil, then repeat **B**.

E Hold a convex lens in front of the camera. Move it backwards and forwards until you get a sharp image.

Real cameras work in the same way as your pinhole camera.

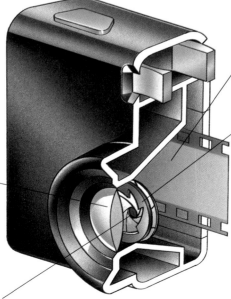

The **film** changes when light reaches it.

The **shutter** stops light getting to the film. It is opened for a very short time when you take a photograph.

The **lens** is used to focus the light. It can be moved in or out to focus on close or distant objects.

The **aperture** is a small hole that lets the light through. Its size can be changed to control the amount of light reaching the film.

Q2 Why is the image dim with a small hole and bright with a big hole?

Q3 Explain what these parts of a camera do
  a the lens
  b the aperture
  c the shutter
  d the film.

Extension exercise 5 can be used now.

17

Using lenses

Lenses are used in many things, such as cameras, **microscopes** and **telescopes**.

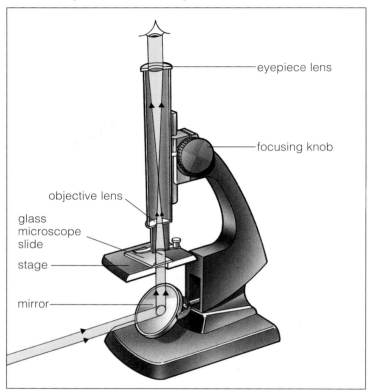

▲ Microscopes are used to look at very small things. The lenses in the microscope make things look bigger.

▲ Scientists who study living things often use microscopes. This is a photograph of a tiny water shrimp.

Astronomers use telescopes to help them study the sky. Telescopes make far away things look bigger.

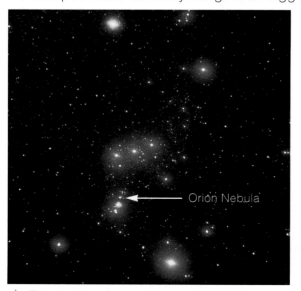

▲ This is the star pattern called Orion.

▲ This is the Orion Nebula. The photograph was taken using a telescope and camera.

Making a telescope

Apparatus

■ fat convex lens ■ thin convex lens
■ metre ruler ■ Blu-Tack

Do not look directly at the Sun. Looking at the Sun directly or through lenses will damage your eyes.

A Stick two lenses to a ruler using Blu-Tack. Put the fat lens at one end, and the thin lens near the other end.

B Look through the lenses, with the fat lens closer to you. Look at something a long way off. Move the thin lens backwards and forwards until you can see a sharp image.

C Look at something closer. Move the thin lens until you get a sharp image again.

Q1 What can we use to:
  a make very small things look bigger?
  b make far away things look bigger?

Q2 How do you focus a telescope?

Extension exercise 6 can be used now.

5. Using our eyes

How our eyes work

Our eyes work like a camera. They have a light sensitive layer and a lens to focus the light.

The **iris** is the coloured part of your eye

The **lens** focuses the light

The **cornea** is transparent to let light through

The **retina** is the light sensitive layer

The **pupil** is a hole in the iris which lets light through

The **optic nerve** sends messages to the brain

The **ciliary muscles** make the lens fatter or thinner

You can make a model eye to stick in your book.

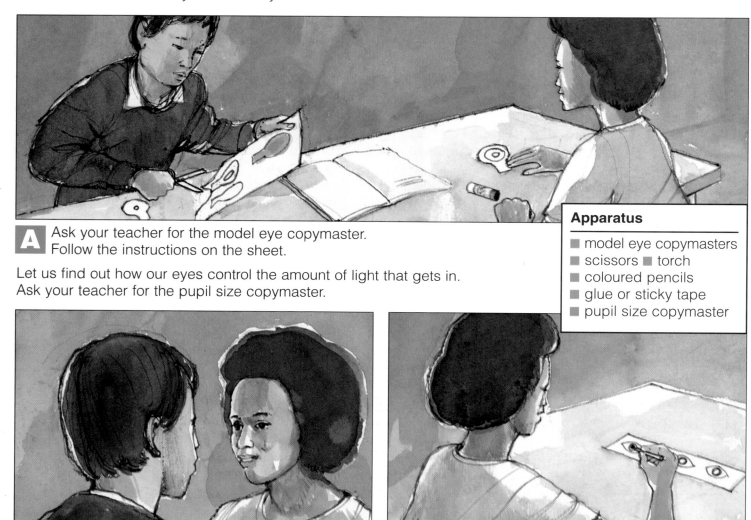

A Ask your teacher for the model eye copymaster. Follow the instructions on the sheet.

Let us find out how our eyes control the amount of light that gets in. Ask your teacher for the pupil size copymaster.

Apparatus
- model eye copymasters
- scissors ■ torch
- coloured pencils
- glue or sticky tape
- pupil size copymaster

B Look at your partner's eyes.

C On your worksheet, draw in the size of his/her pupil in the 'normal light' eye.

D Now shine a torch into your partner's eye for a few seconds. Draw the size of the pupil on the 'bright light' eye.

E Ask your partner to close her/his eyes for two minutes. When he/she opens them, quickly look at the pupil. Fill in the 'dim light' eye.

> **Do not shine the light into anybody's eyes for more than a few seconds. Never shine anything brighter than a torch.**

Eyes and cameras

An eye and a camera both control the amount of light getting in by making a hole bigger or smaller.

You can focus a camera by moving the lens nearer to or further from the film. Our eyes can't do this. The ciliary muscles make the lens fatter or thinner.

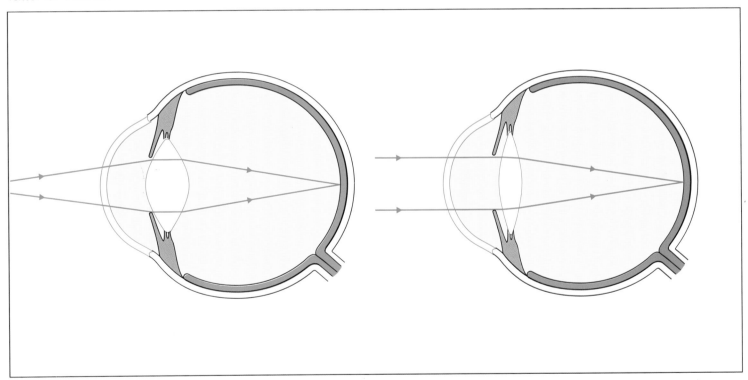

▲ You need a fat lens to focus on near objects.   ▲ You need a thinner lens to focus on distant objects.

Q1 Are the pupils big or small in bright light?

Q2 Are the pupils big or small in dim light?

Q3 Explain why your pupils need to change size.

Q4 Copy this table. Fill in the blank spaces.

What it does	Part of eye	Part of camera
Focuses the light		
Controls the amount of light		
Records a picture		

5. Using our eyes

Long sight and short sight

Most people can see very close and very distant objects. Some people are **short-sighted**. They can see things close to them, but they cannot see distant things clearly. **Long-sighted** people can see distant things but not things near to them.

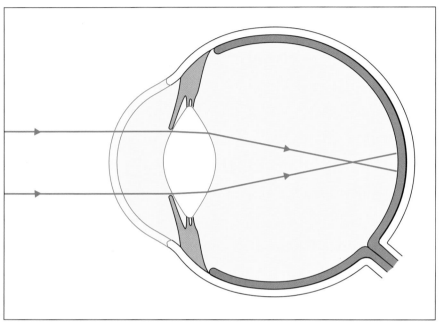

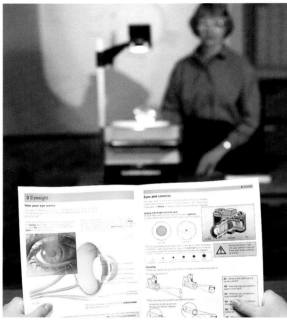

▲ If you are short-sighted the rays of light from distant objects are focused in front of your retina.

▲ This is how things look if you are short-sighted.

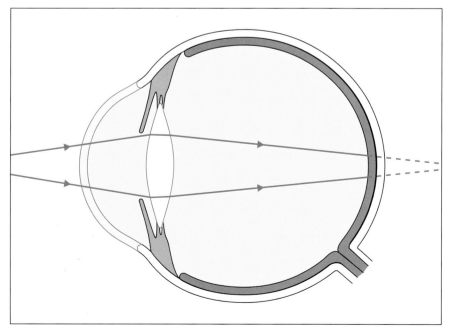

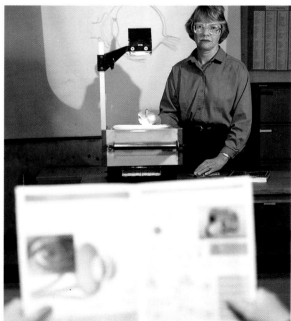

▲ If you are long-sighted the rays of light from close objects are focused behind your retina.

▲ This is how things look if you are long-sighted.

Spectacles can be used to help people see clearly.
Let us find out which kind of lenses are needed.

Q1 Copy this table.

Eyesight problem	Lens needed in spectacles
Short sight	
Long sight	

A Use the short sight copymaster. Your teacher will tell you which lens to stand on the copymaster.

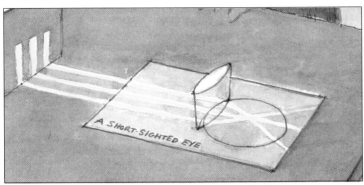

B Use the ray box to shine three rays of light through the lens. The rays of light meet (focus) in front of the retina.

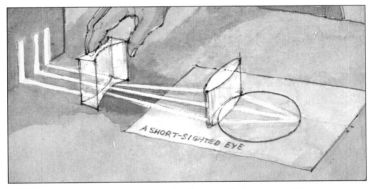

C Stand another lens in front of the eye. Try different lenses to find one that makes the light focus on the retina. Complete the table.

D Use the long sight copymaster. Shine three rays of light through the lens. The rays of light focus behind the retina.

E Repeat **C**. Complete the table.

Q2 Copy these sentences. Choose the correct words from the brackets:

People who have short sight can see only (*close/distant*) things clearly. They need spectacles with (*concave/convex*) lenses to help them see clearly. People who have long sight can see only (*close/distant*) things clearly. They need spectacles with (*concave/convex*) lenses.

Q3 Draw diagrams to show why:
a short-sighted people cannot see distant things clearly
b long-sighted people cannot see near things clearly.

Extension exercise 7 can be used now.

Two eyes are better than one!

Here is an experiment which shows you why we have two eyes.

Having two eyes lets us judge distances. Our brain uses information from both eyes to work out how far away something is.

A Ask a friend to hold out a pencil. Close one eye and try to touch the pencil with your own pencil.

C We can make flat pictures stand out by using coloured filters. Hold a red filter in front of your left eye, and a green filter in front of your right eye. Look at this picture.

The picture seems to stand out because your left eye can see only the green lines, and your right eye can see only the red lines. Each eye is getting a different picture, so it seems to stand out.

Apparatus

- pencil ■ red and green filters
- pictures of animals and birds

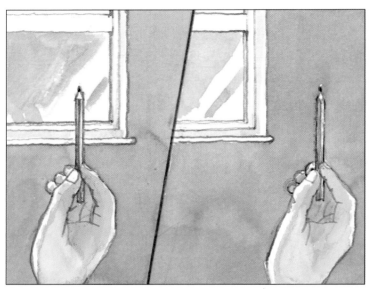

B Hold a pencil in front of you. Close one eye and look at it. Now close the other eye instead. The pencil seems to move. Each eye sees a different picture.

▲ When you look at a box your eyes see slightly different shapes. Your brain combines the pictures to work out how far away the box is.

Your left eye sees this.　　Your right eye sees this.

Q1 Why do we have two eyes instead of just one?

Q2 Make a list of the things it would be difficult to do if we had only one eye.

Q3 Find some pictures of different animals. Make a list of animals or birds that:
a have both eyes on the front of their heads (like cats)
b have eyes on the sides of their heads (like rabbits)
c Is there a pattern? (Hint: think about what the animals eat, or what eats them.)